G000298671

every moment

every moment

A JOURNAL
WITH AFFIRMATIONS

SHAKTI GAWAIN

NEW WORLD LIBRARY

SAN RAFAEL, CALIFORNIA

© 1992 SHAKTI GAWAIN

PUBLISHED BY NEW WORLD LIBRARY

58 PAUL DRIVE

SAN RAFAEL, CA 94903

COVER AND INTERIOR DESIGN AND ILLUSTRATION: KATHY WARINNER

ALL RIGHTS RESERVED. THIS BOOK MAY NOT BE REPRODUCED IN WHOLE
OR IN PART, WITHOUT WRITTEN PERMISSION FROM THE PUBLISHER.

ISBN: 1-880032-11-2

FIRST PRINTING, SEPTEMBER 1992

PRINTED IN THE U.S.A. ON ACID-FREE PAPER

10 9 8 7 6 5 4 3 2 1

DEAR READERS,

JOURNALS CAN BE A VERY HELPFUL TOOL IN
YOUR PROCESS OF DISCOVERING YOURSELF AND
APPRECIATING ALL YOU HAVE BROUGHT INTO
YOUR LIFE TO LEARN FROM. KEEPING A JOURNAL
IS A PRACTICE I HAVE RECOMMENDED FOR A
LONG TIME, AS HAVE MANY IN THE HEALING
PROFESSIONS. MANY OF YOU HAVE ALREADY
BEGUN USING JOURNALS REGULARLY FOR PERSON-
AL GROWTH WORK. WE HAVE PUT TOGETHER THIS
JOURNAL USING AFFIRMATIONS FROM TWO OF
MY PREVIOUS BOOKS, **CREATIVE VISUALIZATION**
AND **REFLECTIONS IN THE LIGHT**, ALONG WITH
THE BEAUTIFUL DESIGNS OF KATHY WARINNER,
IN THE HOPE THAT IT WILL INSPIRE YOU TO SEE
YOUR OWN LIFE AS A WONDERFUL JOURNEY
FILLED WITH LESSONS, BLESSINGS, AND GIFTS.

YOU CAN USE THE AFFIRMATIONS THROUGHOUT
THE DAY IN WHICH YOU READ THEM. YOU CAN
MAKE UP YOUR OWN AFFIRMATION FOR THAT
DAY, OR YOU CAN SIMPLY USE THE AFFIRMATION
AS A STARTING POINT FOR REFLECTING ON YOUR
DAY OR YOUR FEELINGS.

THE ACT OF WRITING YOUR STORY, OR YOUR
GOALS, DREAMS, OR ASPIRATIONS, IS INCREDIBLY
POWERFUL. I HOPE IT WILL HELP YOU TO SEE YOUR
LIFE AS THE WONDERFUL ACT OF CREATION—THE
WORK OF ART—THAT IT IS.

WITH LOVE,

SHAKTI

every moment

EACH DAY I AM CREATING MY LIFE ANEW

MOMENT BY MOMENT, I'M LEARNING TO TRUST THE FLOW OF MY LIFE

I HAVE EVERYTHING I NEED TO ENJOY MY HERE AND NOW

MY LIFE IS BLOSSOMING IN TOTAL PERFECTION

EVERYTHING I NEED IS ALREADY WITHIN ME

I LOVE AND APPRECIATE MYSELF JUST AS I AM

I AM EXPANDING MY IMAGINATION

I AM TALENTED, INTELLIGENT, AND CREATIVE

I EXPRESS MYSELF FREELY, FULLY, AND EASILY

I ACCEPT ALL MY FEELINGS AS PART OF MYSELF

I FEEL HAPPY AND BLISSFUL JUST BEING ALIVE

I AM OPEN TO RECEIVING ALL THE BLESSINGS OF THIS ABUNDANT UNIVERSE!

I AM ALWAYS IN THE RIGHT PLACE AT THE RIGHT TIME, SUCCESSFULLY ENGAGED IN THE RIGHT ACTIVITY

I AM A POWERFUL, LOVING, AND CREATIVE BEING

I AM NOW ATTUNED TO THE DIVINE PLAN OF MY LIFE

LIFE IS MEANT TO BE FUN AND I'M NOW WILLING TO ENJOY IT!

I LIKE TO DO THINGS THAT MAKE ME FEEL GOOD

I AM OPEN TO RECEIVING THE BLESSINGS OF THIS ABUNDANT UNIVERSE

I'M READY NOW TO ACCEPT ALL THE JOY AND PROSPERITY LIFE HAS TO OFFER ME

I GIVE THANKS NOW FOR MY LIFE OF HEALTH, WEALTH, HAPPINESS, AND PERFECT SELF-EXPRESSION

I AM THE MASTER OF MY LIFE

THE LIGHT WITHIN ME IS CREATING MIRACLES IN MY LIFE HERE AND NOW

I'M BEAUTIFUL AND LOVABLE HOWEVER I'M FEELING

ALL MY FEELINGS ARE A NATURAL EXPRESSION OF LIFE

AS I ALLOW MYSELF TO FEEL FEELINGS, I HEAL THEM

I TRUST MY OWN PROCESS

TODAY I AM HONEST, SPONTANEOUS, AND TRUE TO MYSELF

I AM RELAXING AND ENJOYING EVERY MOMENT OF MY LIFE

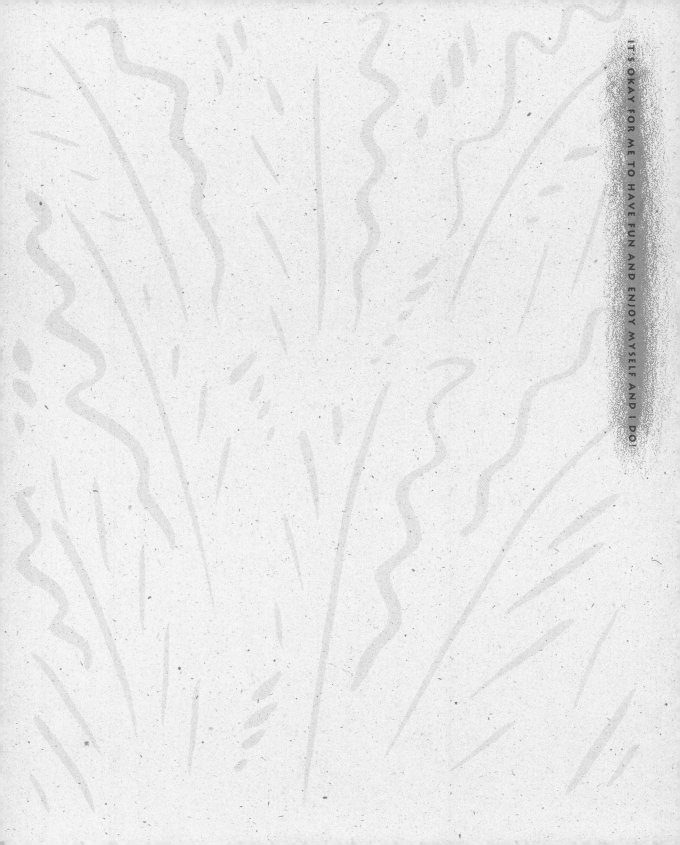

IT'S OKAY FOR ME TO HAVE FUN AND ENJOY MYSELF AND I DO!

AS THE FLOW OF LIFE CHANGES, I CHANGE

IT'S SAFE FOR ME TO RELEASE CONTROL AND EXPERIENCE THE ECSTASY OF LIFE

I TAKE GOOD CARE OF MYSELF

I AM GOOD TO MY BODY, AND MY BODY IS GOOD TO ME

I LOVE AND ACCEPT MY BODY COMPLETELY

I AM NOW FULL OF RADIANT HEALTH AND ENERGY

MY BODY IS A BEAUTIFUL EXPRESSION OF MY SPIRIT

I AM FOLLOWING THE NATURAL RHYTHM OF MY ENERGY

I AM FILLED WITH INNOCENT DELIGHT

THE MORE I LOVE MYSELF, THE MORE LOVE I HAVE TO GIVE OTHERS

I AM FALLING IN LOVE WITH MYSELF

BY BEING MYSELF AND DOING WHAT I LOVE, I MAKE A SIGNIFICANT CONTRIBUTION TO LIFE

MY INNER FEMALE IS NURTURING ME WITH INCREDIBLE LOVE

IT IS SAFE FOR ME TO BE VULNERABLE

THE MORE I RECEIVE, THE MORE I HAVE TO GIVE

THE MORE I RECEIVE, THE MORE OTHERS ARE ABLE TO RECEIVE

THERE IS ENOUGH OF EVERYTHING FOR EVERYONE

I CAN LET GO AND TRUST BECAUSE I KNOW I HAVE EVERYTHING I NEED WITHIN

I LOVE THE WORLD AND THE WORLD LOVES ME

I'M GLAD I WAS BORN AND I LOVE BEING ALIVE

MY IMAGINATION IS A POWERFUL TOOL FOR CREATION

I AM WHOLE AND COMPLETE

DIVINE LOVE AND LIGHT ARE WORKING THROUGH ME NOW

MY INNER WISDOM IS GUIDING ME NOW

THE LIGHT WITHIN ME IS CREATING MIRACLES IN MY BODY, MIND, AND AFFAIRS, HERE AND NOW

THE LIGHT OF GOD WITHIN ME IS PRODUCING PERFECT RESULTS IN EVERY PHASE OF MY LIFE NOW

MY RELATIONSHIPS ARE UNFOLDING IN UNIQUE AND SPECIAL WAYS

I HAVE THE COURAGE TO ASK FOR HELP

I HAVE THE POWER TO HEAL

I ACCEPT AND EMBRACE MY DARKNESS AND MY LIGHT

I ACCEPT MYSELF COMPLETELY HERE AND NOW

I AM A RADIANT EXPRESSION OF GOD

ABOUT THE AUTHOR

SHAKTI GAWAIN'S FIRST BOOK, **CREATIVE VISUAL-IZATION**, HAS SOLD NEARLY TWO MILLION COPIES, WITH FOREIGN EDITIONS IN TWELVE LANGUAGES, AND IS NOW CONSIDERED BY MANY PEOPLE TO BE ONE OF THE BEST SELF-IMPROVEMENT BOOKS EVER WRITTEN. HER SUBSEQUENT BOOKS, **LIVING IN THE LIGHT**, **REFLECTIONS IN THE LIGHT**, **RETURN TO THE GARDEN**, AND **AWAKENING**, HAVE BEEN EQUALLY WELL RECEIVED.

SHAKTI AND HER HUSBAND, JIM BURNS, MAKE THEIR HOME ON KAUAI, HAWAII, WHERE THEY OFFER RETREATS. THEY ALSO LEAD WORKSHOPS THROUGHOUT THE UNITED STATES AND EUROPE.

FOR INFORMATION ABOUT SHAKTI GAWAIN'S WORKSHOPS, WRITE TO:

RIGHT HAND PRODUCTIONS
P.O. BOX 544
MILL VALLEY, CA 94942

OR CALL:
(415) 388-0431

NEW WORLD LIBRARY IS DEDICATED TO PUBLISHING
BOOKS AND CASSETTES THAT HELP IMPROVE THE
QUALITY OF OUR LIVES.

FOR A CATALOG OF OUR FINE BOOKS AND CASSETTES,
CONTACT:

NEW WORLD LIBRARY
58 PAUL DRIVE
SAN RAFAEL, CA 94903
PHONE: (415) 472-2100
FAX: (415) 472-6131

OR CALL TOLL FREE:
(800) 227-3900
IN CALIFORNIA: (800) 632-2122